SIX WORD LESSONS™

FOR SURVIVING A DEVASTATING DIAGNOSIS

100 Lessons

to

Help You Navigate
a Healthcare Crisis

**Shirley Enebrad
Christine Hurley**

Six-Word Lessons for Surviving a Devastating Diagnosis

Published by Pacelli Publishing
9905 Lake Washington Blvd. NE, #D-103
Bellevue, Washington 98004
PacelliPublishing.com

ISBN-10: 1-933750-55-3
ISBN-13: 978-1-933750-55-2

Message to Readers

There are hundreds of diseases in the world. Thankfully not all are fatal. For this book, we address the many challenges of dealing with diagnoses of life-threatening and life-altering illnesses. According to the latest World Health Organization compilation (2012), 14.1 million people were diagnosed with cancer, more than 38,600 per day. Just imagine, cancer is just one category of diseases. If you add in diabetes, cardiovascular, autoimmune system diseases, and HIV, it becomes even more likely that you and your loved ones will need *Six-Word Lessons for Surviving a Devastating Diagnosis.*

Both of us are mothers who dealt with young children diagnosed with cancer. We were forced to learn how to work with healthcare professionals, the corporate systems of large hospitals, and health insurance companies. We know first-hand how illness affects families, careers, friendships and finances. The experiences, reactions to the situations, and our outcomes were very different, but we both came away with a need to help others traveling a similar path.

In ***Six-Word Lessons for Surviving a Devastating Diagnosis***, you will find 100 helpful tips written in simple terms. We want you to have a sense of empowerment as you navigate an uncertain future fraught with unfamiliar surroundings, medical crises, and often toxic treatments.

Upon diagnosis of any serious illness, the fear is immediate and can be unimaginable. Some are T-boned by worries and fear while others accept it and move forward with a sense of trust and ease. Both reactions are normal. There is no one right or wrong way to deal with a serious, life changing illness. But you can educate yourself, learn how to navigate the path thrust upon you and form a support team with family, friends, and professionals.

Our hope is for you to use this little book as a guide to help get you through the curves and pitfalls of your unique journey.

One thing we both learned is "Never underestimate the power of your inner strength and ability to deal with a life challenge. You are stronger than you know."

For more information about Shirley, please go to ShirleyEnebrad.com or email her at Enebrad@6WordLessons.com.

For more information about Christine Hurley, please email IntrepidInterests@gmail.com.

Dedications

My inspiration to coauthor this book comes from experience gained as a patient advocate for several non-profits, living through my son Cory's five-and-a-half-year battle with leukemia, my own cancer diagnosis, my parents' COPD and the disrespect and disregard by doctors, nurses, and whole systems suffered by my brother. I dedicate this book to Bobby Enebrad with the hope others will be better equipped to survive a frightening diagnosis. Praise and admiration go to those doctors and nurses who treat their patients with kindness respect and compassion.

Special mahalo (thanks) to Patty and Lonnie Pacelli for once again assisting my effort to honor Cory's directive to help others. Huge hugs and mahalo to Nancy Miller for your valuable input based on your life experiences. *--Shirley Enebrad*

This book is dedicated to all the wonderful family, friends, and professionals who helped us through our journey, directly and indirectly. This includes Sue Ehling, ARNP and Douglas Hawkings, MD. My daughter would not be alive today without your love and dedication to care and continued research of childhood cancers. Rhonda Zuick, Shirley Enebrad, and many others not mentioned who provided friendship, support, love, laughter, and more. Each of you helped make the journey not only easier and joyful but successful in many ways. I am also forever thankful to God for His continuous miracles in our lives. **--*Christine Hurley***

Contents

Symptoms to Watch for and Why

1

You just don't feel very well.

You feel off. It could be a virus or infection. Persistent headaches, fever, unexplained aches, and bruises are some of the signs that you should see your doctor. Don't try to self-diagnose. Don't Google it. Get to the doctor.

You are not acting like yourself.

Changes in personality, suspicious thoughts, high strung when once calm, and paranoia are all signs that something is wrong. It might mean you are ill or if you take medications, those can be off. If a loved one expresses concern, don't dismiss his or her assertions without considering a medical examination.

You suddenly gain or lose weight.

Sudden weight change might be a sign that your metabolism is being adversely affected by a physical abnormality. If you or a loved one notices that your clothes don't fit the same, weigh yourself immediately and keep track of losses or gains. Get checked out!

You're sluggish, tired, with no energy.

If you are normally active but suddenly stuck on the couch for no apparent reason, pay attention. Your energy level fluctuates by how healthy or unhealthy you are. Don't ignore this important indicator when you bottom out.

Food just doesn't taste very good.

Suddenly your taste buds dislike all your favorite foods. If there is a drastic difference in flavor such as your normal foods taste bitter, metallic, weird or just plain unappealing, you should see your doctor.

You have not been sleeping well.

Changes in your sleep pattern can contribute to energy loss. Lack of sleep can also make your brain fuzzy or cause dizziness. If you cannot connect the dots to discern why your sleep is bad, it is time to look for answers. Get help from a healthcare professional.

Noticeably different temperature in your body

If you experience temperature differences in your limbs or body, you need to get checked out right away. Keep track of when you noticed the hot or cold sensations, and what you were doing at the time. You will want to give your doctor an accurate picture of what's happening to you.

Your vision changes or gets blurry.

Changes in your vision can mean many different things. Whatever your symptoms, write them down and describe what happened, where you were and what you were doing. Get to your doctor as soon as possible.

You have sudden swelling or tenderness.

There are many things that can cause swelling or tenderness. If persistent, it is important to let your physician know when you first noticed it, and where the swelling or pain occurred, especially if you don't recall injuring yourself.

10

Persistent sores/wounds or dry patches

Always get sores or a dry patch of skin or a thickened spot looked at if there are no signs of healing after a few days. If it goes away and reappears in the same spot, you need to see your doctor and get a referral to a dermatologist.

You Get the Diagnosis, Now What?

11

Find best treatment team for you.

You can choose your own doctor. You don't have to stay with your diagnosing physician. You want to find the best doctor in the field. You will have to put effort into that and not worry about hurt feelings. You are in charge of your health.

12

Ask everyone you know for recommendations.

Treatment centers vary in their focus. If possible, find out which ones might be studying your particular disease and situation. Medical advances are happening all the time, and you want the most knowledgeable team possible.

13

Google doctor's name, reviews, and complaints.

There are ways to find out about a doctor's history such as websites dedicated to doctors' histories, newspaper archives, and your state's health department. Check thoroughly. Ask for references.

14

Don't choose by location and convenience.

There is a big, wide world out there you can tap into, so don't just settle for a treatment center because it is more convenient. Find the best doctor and facility in your area or beyond. Your life could depend on it.

15

Be sure to get another opinion.

We repeat, there is nothing wrong with insisting on a second opinion. It is in your best interest to have confirmation of your diagnosis and another opinion on the treatment options. Not all doctors read and interpret test results or treatment protocols the same.

16

Decide whose personality fits yours best.

You want someone who treats you with respect. One who will call you back promptly and not leave you waiting. You need a doctor who loves what he or she does. You should choose a doctor who is caring, kind, and knowledgeable.

17

Ask pointed questions and check reactions.

You can determine a lot about how the doctor is going to work with you based on the questions you ask and the way she or he answers them. Ask how many patients the doctor has treated with your diagnosis and about their outcomes.

18

You don't want arrogant, egotistical doctors.

Don't just blindly trust that he or she is the best doctor for your case. Pay attention to bedside manner. You will be putting your life in the hands of this person and depending on him or her to get you through this nightmare to a positive outcome.

19

Mutual respect and cooperation are key.

Who you choose to monitor your case should be decided by you. You need to feel confident you made the best choice. You want someone who is trustworthy and has the skills and temperament to walk beside you and guide you through this difficult time.

20

Establish mutual goals with clear understanding.

Determine your treatment goals together. Be an active participant. You must also be realistic about what you can and cannot expect from your doctor. Speak up. Ask how he or she sees your treatment journey and how much you can expect from the patient doctor relationship. Co-lead your care.

Create Support for Your Entire Family

21

Communicate openly with family and friends.

No matter which role you find yourself in, whether patient, caregiver or family member, support is key. Reach out to friends and family. Ask for what you need from them. People want to help. They will follow your lead. So you need to give clear instructions. Guide them. Let them feel useful to you and your family.

22

Create ground rules for your family.

Make your expectations about behavior clear. Everyone will be stressed out and scared, so make rules about acceptable ways to act out and communicate. Speak the truth about your feelings. If your family isn't good at speaking their minds in the best of times you must find a way to communicate comfortably.

23

Identify advocates within the treatment team.

Link up with social workers, nurses and other advocates within your healthcare system. You might start with your social worker. Based on previous experience with others in similar situations, the social worker usually understands your needs.

24

Support at your place of employment

Speak with your supervisor and be as honest as you can about your situation. Ask your supervisor or manager for support regarding any time off you need for medical appointments. Ask if you can telecommute so you can continue working.

25

Surround yourself with positive, supportive people.

Staying positive makes a huge difference. Ask people to treat you as if you were not ill. Concentrate on being in the moment and making the most of each one.

26

Support groups at your treatment facility.

Most treatment centers offer support groups. Ask your doctor, nurse or social worker to recommend one. Try it at least twice to see if you get any benefit from being around others with your diagnosis or who are in a similar situation.

27

Online support can be helpful too.

If you are not a "sit around a room with others" type of person, or if you just don't feel up to going to a group, look for an online support group. E-support is accessible from anywhere, and you don't have to worry about being pressured to share if you are not ready.

28

Get professional help when it's needed.

There are thousands of therapists who can help you. Be sure you look for someone with the proper credentials who has been highly educated and trained. Your social worker should know of some, or you can search on internet sites such as *Psychology Today* or *Health Grades*.

29

Most employers have Employee Assistance Programs.

Your Human Resources contact will have the telephone number for an EAP therapist/psychologist who can help you and your family. He or she will have a list of those who accept your insurance. Using the list can save you time.

30

Research, read everything and reach out.

Remember, if what you find is written by a lay person, you need to check it out with your doctor. He or she should support your desire to know everything about your illness, and how to give you the proper information to make informed decisions.

Know Your Treatment and Side Effects

31

Listen carefully to the doctor's description.

At the time of diagnosis, you will likely be nervous and possibly in shock. Ask questions. Use your cell phone or bring a recorder. Record the doctor if possible because you will want to go back later to hear it again. You will only retain about 30 percent of what is said.

32

Ask for written descriptions of treatment.

The doctor should have a booklet or pamphlet that describes the treatment you will be receiving. If he or she is giving you options, you need to find out the differences between the medications and each one's risk factors. Pharmacists are very knowledgeable about drugs, their side effects, and possible benefits.

33

Invite another listener to accompany you.

It can be very helpful to have a friend or family member with a less emotional pair of ears join you to take notes, handle the recording or ask questions. Your trusted listener might think of questions you haven't. You can also use the support.

Educate yourself on latest treatment options.

Do your homework. Educate yourself on possible treatments which might enhance or replace what your doctor suggested. You can ask for another meeting to discuss your findings with the doctor. Do not feel as if you are difficult. It's your life.

35

Contemplate the risks versus the benefits.

It is important to undertand the risks. With each medication, there are bound to be side effects. Be proactive. Find out what you can expect from each one and how to alleviate any ill effects. Again, a pharmacist has valuable knowledge of medications and possible side effects.

Medicinal pot can be your friend.

Many people are opposed to using pot, but now that it is legal recreationally in several states and used medicinally in many more, you should consider the positive uses. It can jump start your appetite which is always affected by medications. Pot can also curb nausea and vomiting.

37

Try to maintain normal family activities.

Your mental health can be affected by treatment and its side effects. It isn't easy, but try to maintain normal activities with your family. It can boost your mood to participate even as a bystander when you observe loved ones performing, playing sports, or just reading a book.

38

Focus your energies on staying positive.

Don't let the illness consume your life. It is hard when not feeling well, but you must focus on living well. Stay connected to your loved ones and be good to yourself. Make long-term plans for the future.

39

Find out how other patients coped.

Side effects are often different for each patient. If you attend a support group you may get useful tips as to how others dealt with side effects. Hearing how others fared can alleviate the fear of the unknown too. There are support groups for family members too.

40

Investigate alternative remedies and Eastern medicine.

We are not suggesting you abandon Western medicine, but complementary treatments can enhance your care. There are teas, juices, vitamin supplements, body work, massage, or acupuncture which might help you cope with harsh treatments, keep your body chemistry more balanced and your energy level up, or even help you sleep.

Keep Family Drama Down, Spirits Up!

41

Educate the whole family about treatment.

It works best if everyone in the family knows what you will be going through and the possible risks. If your medication makes your hair fall out or your skin break out it would be best to know in advance. Fear of the unknown is far worse than reality.

42

Don't judge how others are coping.

Your normal is not necessarily someone else's. Even if you are the patient, try to understand that your loved ones may be unable to deal with strong emotions such as fear. Check in with each loved one regularly to see how each is coping.

43

Don't be embarrassed about wants/needs.

Ask for what you want. Put yourself first. Do what is best for you. For example, it isn't selfish if you need time alone to grieve or process your emotions. Don't hold back. Speak up to get your needs met.

44

During this time keep drama out.

It is easy to get frustrated, scared and angry over your current situation, which can lead you to vent on family, friends or coworkers, and vice versa. Don't allow negative situations to control you. Work together to stay positive and loving.

Talk about your feelings and fears.

Encourage openness with your loved ones. If you start the dialogue, it will help family members to share as well. Make your thoughts, needs and fears clear so everyone can understand what is happening and process together.

46

When someone is hurting, be there.

Whether you are the patient or a loved one, provide love and support to those around you. Keep your loved ones close. Don't push away those who are being difficult as they are hurting too. Watch the quiet ones. It isn't healthy to internalize.

47

Remember to be kind to yourself.

Patients and caregivers, don't put yourself last. Give yourself a break and try not to blame yourself for causing others to worry or if you feel as if you are not doing enough. Live one day at a time. Think positively. Visualize a return to good health.

48

Laugh as often as you can.

Laughter is important. Try to look for humor in all situations. Avoid negative people and choose to surround yourself with those who have positive attitudes. If you can't avoid negative people, minimize your time spent with them.

49

Try to maintain your family's normal.

If you can keep some semblance of your family's normal activities, it helps. If you normally have family meals, continue that time of togetherness, even if you can't eat. Stick to your family's routines as much as possible.

50

If problems arise, get professional help.

Get someone to mediate if your family is having problems communicating. Sometimes you just need someone with a neutral perspective to listen and help you sort through the muck. It could be a therapist, minister or a trusted friend.

Finances, Fees, Forms, Fails and Fixes

51

You cannot afford to be sick.

Bodies react to stress adversely. Finances are devastated by expensive treatments for illness. There will be time lost from work. Set your priorities and if necessary ask someone to help you sort out payment plans.

52

How to tackle piles of paperwork.

Keep a specific file cabinet. Make separate files for treatment reports, notes from doctor meetings, invoices from doctors, hospitalizations, and pharmacy expenses. Keep track of your mileage to and from treatments and other appointments for your taxes too.

53

Learn how to protect your assets.

If the diagnosis requires a long or expensive treatment protocol, consult an accountant or a lawyer about how to protect your family's assets and still be able to utilize all available resources.

54

Who should you ask for help?

Ask if your treatment facility has financial advisors for patients. If not, consult an accountant who is familiar with medical expenses. Ask if there is a patient advocate who can assist with finding you help. Some employers' EAP departments can help.

55

Prescription medications can break the bank.

Explore free medication programs that might help patients get medication directly from manufacturers. Pharma.org/patients is one. See the list of helpful websites at the end of the book.

56

Creative ways to find monetary assistance

Check with Social Security, Veterans benefits, your church. Service organizations such as Kiwanis, Eagles, Rotary, VFW, the Lions Club, and Shriners might also offer assistance. Look for diagnosis-specific organizations too.

57

Insurance companies have specialists to help.

Call to find out who specifically is handling your claim. Or ask if they have a Benefits Specialist who can help you navigate the system to ensure you will receive needed treatment. It never hurts to negotiate with your provider.

58

What if you don't have insurance?

If you have no coverage, contact your state's Department of Health and Social Services to see what is available. You might need your doctor to write a letter on your behalf. If all else fails, your friends and family can do fundraisers, or use online funding sites.

59

Financial stress can impact your recovery.

The best way to alleviate financial stress is to delegate someone else to help keep your books and records in order, watch for billing errors, and keep all correspondence related to your treatment filed. If you don't have such a person, ask at your bank, or ask your clergy member for a recommendation.

60

Clinical trials might be the answer.

Ask your doctor if he or she knows of any clinical trials on your type of illness. Find out what the risks versus benefits might be. There could be great financial relief with little risk. But more often than not you must carefully decide whether or not to proceed.

You Must Strive to Stay Positive

61

Tough times are temporary and finite.

Going through treatment may feel as if it will never end, but it will. Treatment is a temporary challenge. When negative feelings start to surface, find ways to help counter the negativity by reading a good book, picking up a hobby, or talking to a trusted friend. Music helps too.

62

Find the good; it's always there.

No matter how bad the situation, always strive to find the good. Challenge yourself to find three positives things per day. After a month of doing this, you will begin to feel and see a difference in your outlook. Create a gratitude journal.

63

Help from others can alleviate stress.

It can be difficult accepting help from others, especially if you are the independent type. People don't help with the intention of adding a burden. They help because they want to and because they care. Accept gracefully and know you will pay it forward someday.

64

Real friends are very special people.

Your real friends stick by you through challenging times, regardless of the distance. You have a shared history. They can make you laugh or make you cry. They will also make you feel loved and needed. You may make new friends during this difficult time. Savor them all.

65

Trust your family during difficult times.

The support of your spouse, siblings, parents, and immediate family can help keep you positive through treatment. Their love can keep you from getting depressed. Strong relationships with family and mending old hurts from the past can be helpful.

66

Always remember you are not alone.

If you need support, remember that you are not alone. Reach out to a trusted friend or a counselor, or find online discussion boards where others are sharing similar stories. Support groups can be helpful too. Stay connected.

67

Remain faithful, trust in your path.

This one can be tough. Regardless of your religion or faith, there are some remarkable stories of people who have held joy in their hearts, trusted in a higher entity, and remained faithful even in their darkest days. Look for inspiration.

68

Self-replenishing time away is necessary.

You need to take care of you. To do that, you may feel the need to have a weekend retreat to reflect and replenish. Whether it is at home as a stay-cation or a short distance away at a local Bed & Breakfast, this is the time to take care of you. Get away as often as you can.

69

Smile in the face of fear.

It's easy to be anxious and filled with worry, especially now. Instead, choose to be courageous and brave. Don't let your fear rob you of the potential joy in your life. Happiness can help you overcome fear. It isn't easy but you can do it!

70

You are stronger than you know.

At first you may have doubted your ability and strength to cope. Regardless of whether you are the patient or the caretaker, you will find the strength to get through, even in your moments of weakness. Think positively. By taking one step at a time, you can conquer fear.

Confront Conflicts Caused by Your Illness

71

Treatment/illness may affect your job.

Treatment can affect memory and cause fatigue. Talk to your supervisor about realigning your schedule. Working from home, trading positions with a coworker or job sharing for a period may help you.

72

Family dynamics may change during illness.

During times of stress, many families get closer, but the chaos and tension can tear families apart. Problems may arise over treatment decisions. Some might feel left out. Educate your family. Strive for family unity. Be a team.

73

Be aware of signs of depression.

Be conscious of sadness, crankiness, or problems with sleep, appetite, feelings of despair, lack of motivation and low energy. Social isolation can also lead to depression. Feelings of depression are common during this time. Talk to your doctor.

74

Religious or spiritual conflicts impacting treatment

Sometimes your family's religious beliefs may conflict with the doctor's advice. Find another physician, a pastor or a third party to help you navigate or negotiate the right treatment path for you.

It is okay
to be angry.

Letting go of things such as sports, dancing, dining out, hanging out with friends, and just being yourself can hurt. Not everyone will stand by you. That hurts. Your whole life has changed. More pain. It is okay to be angry but don't let it define you.

76

Unexpected side effects may cause confusion.

When taking a new medication, you may experience unexpected side effects. Report them immediately to your doctor. Your team may need to explore alternatives. Communicate with your doctor. Do not self-diagnose.

77

Find a distraction from side effects.

Side effects can be miserable, especially if you focus on them. Find a good distraction from the discomfort. Do what you enjoy. Find a hobby. Learn something new such as a foreign language, or how to play an instrument. Be creative.

78

When trust issues develop, now what?

Determine the root cause. Explore ways to correct the issue and continue with treatment. If you can't find a way to mend the trust issues within your team, you will need to go elsewhere. Lack of trust can impact your overall success.

79

Alternative medicines can interfere with pharmaceuticals.

Do not take alternatives to your doctor's prescriptions without first informing your team. Many supplements can interfere with medications prescribed by your physician. The team can advise you.

80

Cultural differences between you and doctors

Your physician's job is to treat you, but sometimes cultural differences may interfere. Speak up and confront the issue. If you have difficulty with this, ask for help through family, friends, or the treatment center's ombudsman.

Face Your Future and Ongoing Issues

81

Find out what to expect now.

Ask what your new normal will now be. Find out what, if any, long-term side effects might occur from your treatment such as surgeries, chemotherapy, and radiation. Ask what follow-up tests or medications will be required and for approximately how long.

82

Life goes on even though different.

There are things that you will be able to do again now that treatment is over. Be cautious, though, as it would be safest to take your time and make sure you are up for each activity before jumping right back in.

83

You must adapt to life changes.

There might be activities you can no longer do. You might need help to accept those changes. Focus on what you can do. Get help for those you cannot. There are medical assistance products for nearly all disabilities.

84

Facing mortality can make you fearful.

It is very common for people who have faced their mortality to become fearful about it happening again. You must learn how to calm yourself. If you need help, a trained therapist can teach you.

85

Helping others can be very rewarding.

Your experience may help someone else in the same or a similar situation. Don't underestimate the impact you can have on someone else. Even speaking honestly and openly at a support group is helpful. It's a win-win.

86

Work with the employer on schedule needs.

Ask your employer to let you assimilate back into your routine incrementally. Don't try to do it all at once. Take your time, because you might still tire easily. You might have brain fuzziness from the treatments and won't be functioning at 100 percent for awhile.

87

You still need your loved ones.

Appreciate and praise those who have supported you throughout your illness and recovery. Make sure they know what you still need from them. Coordinate with them on your new normal. Show them how grateful you are for the support.

88

Adjust to your new routine slowly.

Your body's response to treatment and the side effects can take a while to subside. Don't expect to feel "normal" or as you did pre-illness right away. Be patient, give yourself lots of time to recover, and continue to think positively.

89

Plan your life, don't look back.

You probably had a lot of time to consider what is important to you and what makes your life valuable. Keep moving forward and try to focus on the future. Don't dwell on the past. Give yourself credit for surviving.

90

Celebrate your successes; you deserve it.

Don't be afraid or shy about celebrating the fact that you survived a terrible illness with very harsh treatment, whether it was surgery, chemotherapy or radiation. You won't jinx yourself. Just be happy it's over.

What if Treatment Fails to Cure?

91

Some serious diseases are not curable.

Multiple Sclerosis, Parkinson's and other diseases are not curable. Doctors can treat symptoms or even slow down the progression with medication. Work with your healthcare team to find the best medications and methods for you to navigate your illness.

92

Your doctor says no more treatment.

Ask what that means exactly. Ask if there are any experimental treatments and if you might fit the criteria to participate. Do your research to see what might be available in other countries. Don't give up without trying.

93

Talk to your loved ones immediately.

Do not leave your loved ones in the dark. Include your family and friends right away. You will need to support each other. And if you decide to pursue new options, they can help with research.

94

Put your house in order now.

Line up in-home nursing or hospice care for when it is needed. Sort out your insurance coverage. Take the time to get organized, so it can free you up to concentrate on your relationships and to live fully longer.

95

Get legal and financial files organized.

Make sure that your legal obligations and your will are in order. Designate an executor. Make a list of all User IDs, passwords, bank accounts, stock portfolio, and insurance policies. Give your closest family member the information to keep for you.

96

Speak with family about your desires.

Don't be afraid to speak with your family about what you would like them to do to honor your last wishes. Tell them if you want a burial, cremation or to donate your body to science. Make it clear, so there are no misunderstandings or family problems later.

97

Write letters to your loved ones.

If it is too difficult to speak openly with your loved ones, you can put your thoughts and feelings down on paper or have someone record your likeness for you. Written or recorded messages are especially nice for saying goodbye to young ones.

98

Make happy memories with loved ones.

No matter how much time you have, make as many happy memories with your loved ones as possible. Show them how much you care and give them the gift of spending time with you. Express how you feel. Celebrate your life!

99

Work with a family grief specialist.

Early on select a therapist, counselor or coach who specializes in death and dying. He or she will help support the patient and loved ones through the anticipated grief and the actual death process when the time comes.

100

Crossing over the rainbow bridge preparations.

You get to decide what you want your last experience to be and with whom you want to share it. Speak up and make your desires clear. Do not worry about hurt feelings. This time is truly all about you.

Helpful websites

Drugs.com/sfx
Resource for drug side effects. Just enter the drug name, and it will give you a complete list of possible side effects.

MayoClinic.org/symptom-checker/select-symptom/itt-20009075
Good symptom checker

MentalHealthAmerica.net/prescription-assistance
Find options for medication payment assistance

ConsumerReports.org/health/resources/pdf/best-buy-drugs/money-saving-guides/english/AssistancePrograms.pdf
A medication assistance website

ncbi.nlm.nih.gov/pubmed
Research diseases, treatments, medicines and more

WebMD.com
Provides health information and tools for health management

About the *Six-Word Lessons Series*

Legend has it that Ernest Hemingway was challenged to write a story using only six words. He responded with the story, "For sale: baby shoes, never worn." The story tickles the imagination. Why were the shoes never worn? The answers are left up to the reader's imagination.

This style of writing has a number of aliases: postcard fiction, flash fiction, and micro fiction. Lonnie Pacelli was introduced to this concept in 2009 by a friend, and started thinking about how this extreme brevity could apply to today's communication culture of text messages, tweets and Facebook posts. He wrote the first book, *Six-Word Lessons for Project Managers*, then started helping other authors write and publish their own books in the series.

The books all have six-word chapters with six-word lesson titles, each followed by a one-page description. They can be written by entrepreneurs who want to promote their businesses, or anyone with a message to share.

See the entire *Six-Word Lessons Series* at 6wordlessons.com

Made in the USA
Columbia, SC
18 May 2018